Hong Kong Capers
香港歷險記

Written and illustrated by Jill Wild

O'Donald
Publications
愛的路出版社

For
Sarah and Peter

My thanks to Ian for his support, Jean for her help and Jackie for making it happen.

J.

Published in Hong Kong 1999
by O'Donald Publications.

Jill Wild
P.O.Box 11615
General Post Office
Hong Kong

ISBN 962-8159-05-4

Printed by Teleprint
Telefax: 2525 7666

It all started just after Mum called you for breakfast. Remember?

We'd been watching the fountain at the Peak and I was sitting beside you. When you got up you knocked me off that little bench we were sitting on and you ran off without me, you left me there

all alone.

Now, you know how windy it can get on the Peak, well, one big gust sent me rolling over and over.

I nearly hit the wall but...

...somehow I shot right through a drainage hole.

Too bad about the drop at the other side.

I fell straight onto the Peak Tram track and started to slide, ever so slowly at first, until

ZING

I got faster and faster until the fur on my bottom was smoking.

I hoped you'd be there to catch me at the bottom of the track, but...

...I bounced.
I didn't know
I was a
bouncy sort
of bear
but,
I bounced.

And landed on top
of a street cleaner's hat.

It wasn't until we reached the Botanical Gardens that disaster struck.

The street cleaner tipped her head back and down I fell.

I was about to land in the gutter when...

THONK

I suddenly found myself in the company of a large number of chickens. They were huddled together in a basket, on the front of a bike, on their way to market.

It was not a very comfortable ride, it was bumpy, the air was smelly from the traffic fumes and the chickens talked non-stop all the way to Wan Chai Market.

When we got to the market the man who'd been pedalling the bike unloaded the chickens at one of the meat stalls, but he didn't seem too pleased to see me.

He picked me up by my leg and flung me across the market.

I felt like a furry Frisbee. It's a shame you weren't there to catch me.

I wasn't sure

whether I'd land on a vegetable stall or in amongst some hard looking green bananas. I rather fancied the choi sum, it looked the softest, but no,

oh no,

it wasn't to be.

I landed in a white plastic carrier bag containing a large, wet, slippery, slimy mullet.

Ugh, I hate fish.

The lady carrying the fish took us on a very crowded tram.

And the mullet and I got so squashed together, I ended up wearing a couple of it's fish scales as contact lenses.

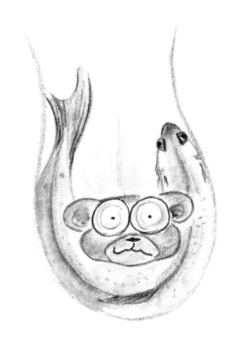

Thankfully, after a few minutes the tram stopped with a jolt. I was thrown clean out of the bag

THUMP

and bashed straight into the back of a tourist's rucksack. The fur on my back stuck fast to the Velcro fastening on his rucksack and there I hung until he got off the tram at Causeway Bay.

The tourist and I strolled over to look at the Noon Day Gun.

As he lent up against it, my fur peeled painfully away from the Velcro and I slid very gently down the barrel of the gun. It was dark and peaceful in there until midday when...

Flying high over Victoria Harbour was quite enjoyable and I had a wonderful view of the Star Ferries busily to-ing and fro-ing across the bay.

I hoped that you might be on one of them and that you'd see me and rescue me.

If the wind had been just a little bit stronger I think I might have made it all the way to Tsim Sha Tsui but...

SPLOSH

I landed in the grey green sea.

The next thing I remember, I was being pulled out of the water into a battered old sampan with a fish hook stuck in my ear. Then I was tossed into a wicker basket full of flapping fish.

Ugh, I hate fish.

The sampan bobbed along all the way to the Jumbo Floating Restaurant and by this time my fur was soggy, slimy and stank of fish.

Perhaps it was this awful smell that attracted the big brown bird that kept circling around me (I think you once told me they were called kites).

The kite dived down and grabbed me round the tummy with it's very sharp talons. It carried me higher and higher and further and further from the sea and I thought that I would never see you again.

But as we circled around, I began to realise that I knew exactly where we were. We were flying round and round the Peak. Somewhere down there you were eating lunch whilst way up here I was being lunch!

If only you'd looked up you would have seen what happened next. The kite gave me a vicious peck on the nose but when he found it was only plastic he dropped me in disgust.

It was a very long way down and I landed

SPLAT

face first on the hard ground right back where I started from by the fountain at the Peak.

And there I lay until just now when you came running back to look for me.

So perhaps now you'll understand why I don't sound too excited about going to Ocean Park.

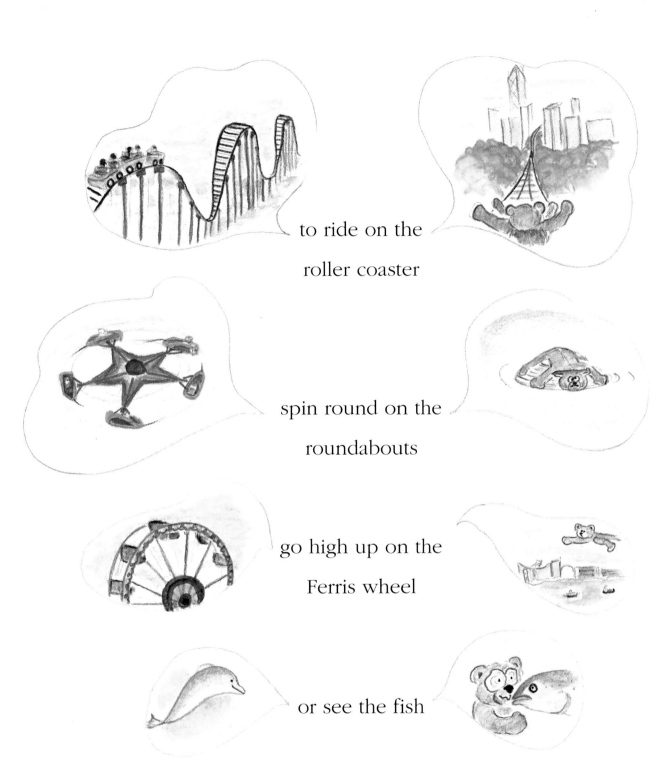

to ride on the roller coaster

spin round on the roundabouts

go high up on the Ferris wheel

or see the fish

Ugh, I hate fish

I think I'll just sit quietly and watch.